LATIN
Playalong *for* Alto Saxophone

Exclusive Distributors:
Hal Leonard Europe Limited
42 Wigmore Street
Marylebone, London, W1U 2RY
Email: info@halleonardeurope.com

Hal Leonard Australia Pty. Ltd.
4 Lentara Court
Cheltenham, Victoria, 3192 Australia
Email: info@halleonard.com.au

Order No. AM966075
ISBN 0-7119-8367-4
This book © Copyright 2001 by Hal Leonard.

Compiled by Nick Crispin.
Music arranged by Jack Long.
Music processed by Enigma Music Production Services.
Cover photography by George Taylor.
Printed in the EU.

CD produced by Music By Design.
Instrumental solos by John Whelan.
Engineered by Kester Sims.

Saxophone Fingering Chart

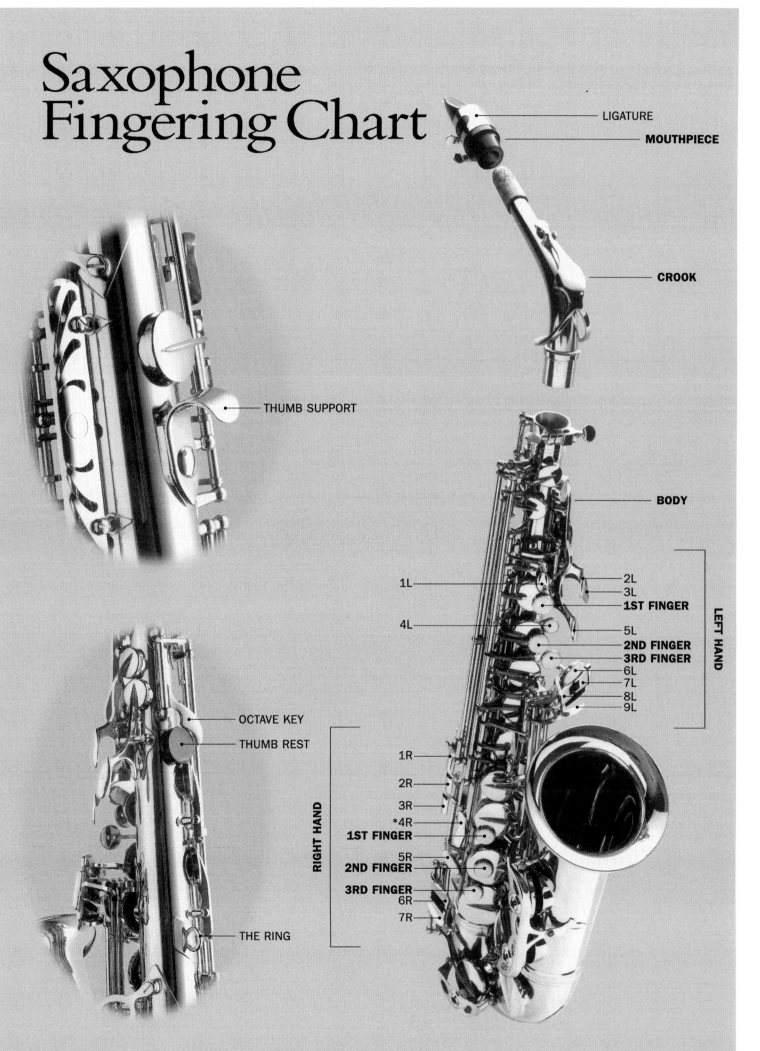

LIGATURE

MOUTHPIECE

CROOK

THUMB SUPPORT

BODY

1L

2L
3L
1ST FINGER

4L

5L
2ND FINGER
3RD FINGER
6L
7L
8L
9L

LEFT HAND

OCTAVE KEY

THUMB REST

1R

2R

3R

*4R

1ST FINGER

5R
2ND FINGER

3RD FINGER
6R

7R

RIGHT HAND

THE RING

* Not fitted on some saxophones

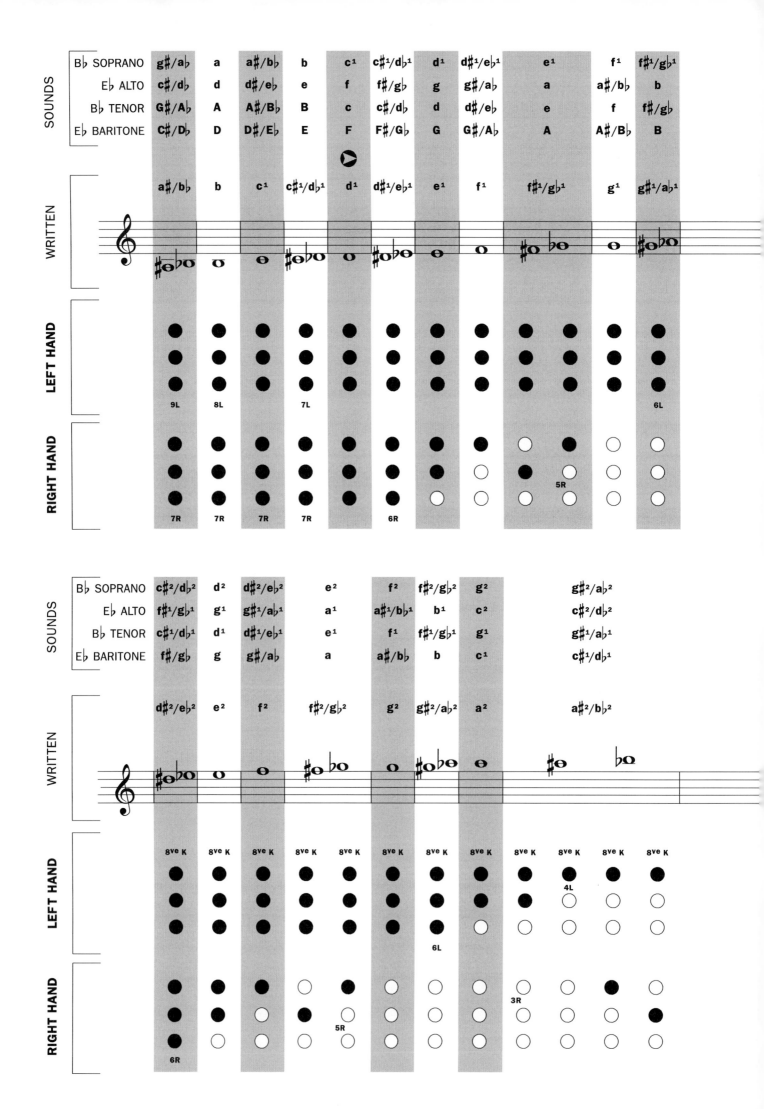

Indicates the lower limit of the best playing range

Indicates the upper limit of the best playing range

Dos Gardenias

Words & Music by Isolina Carrillo

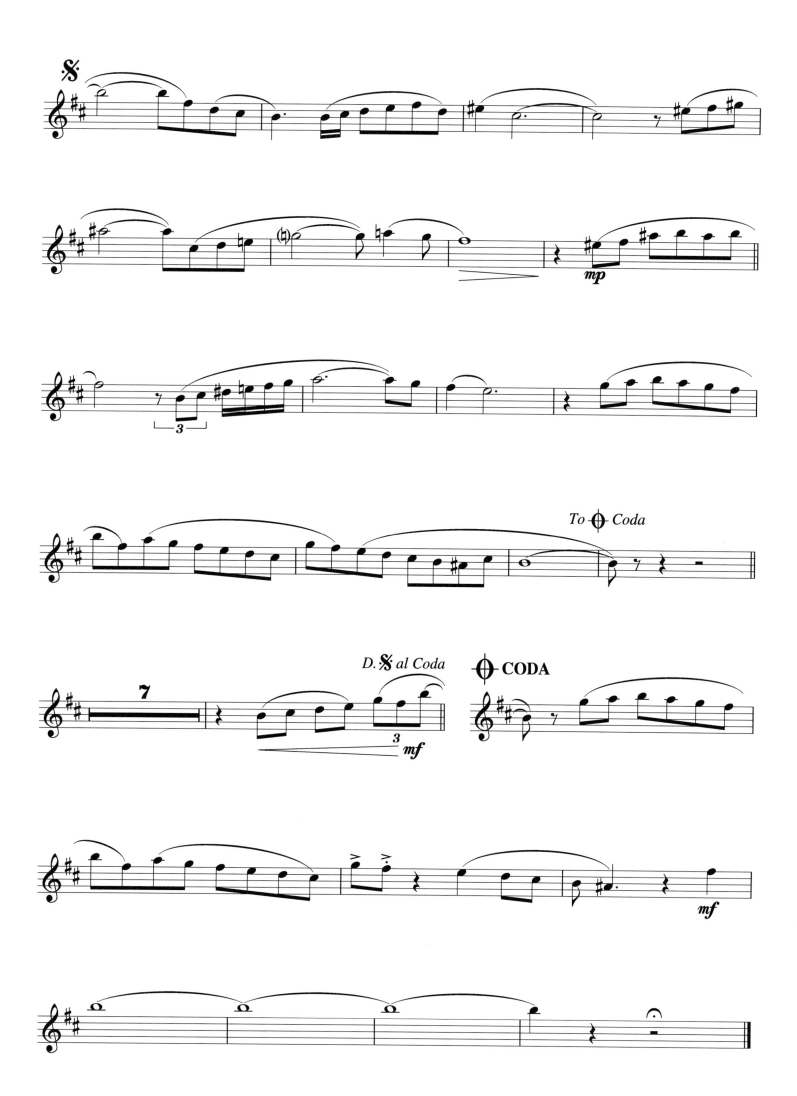

Besame Mucho

Words & Music by Consuelo Velazquez

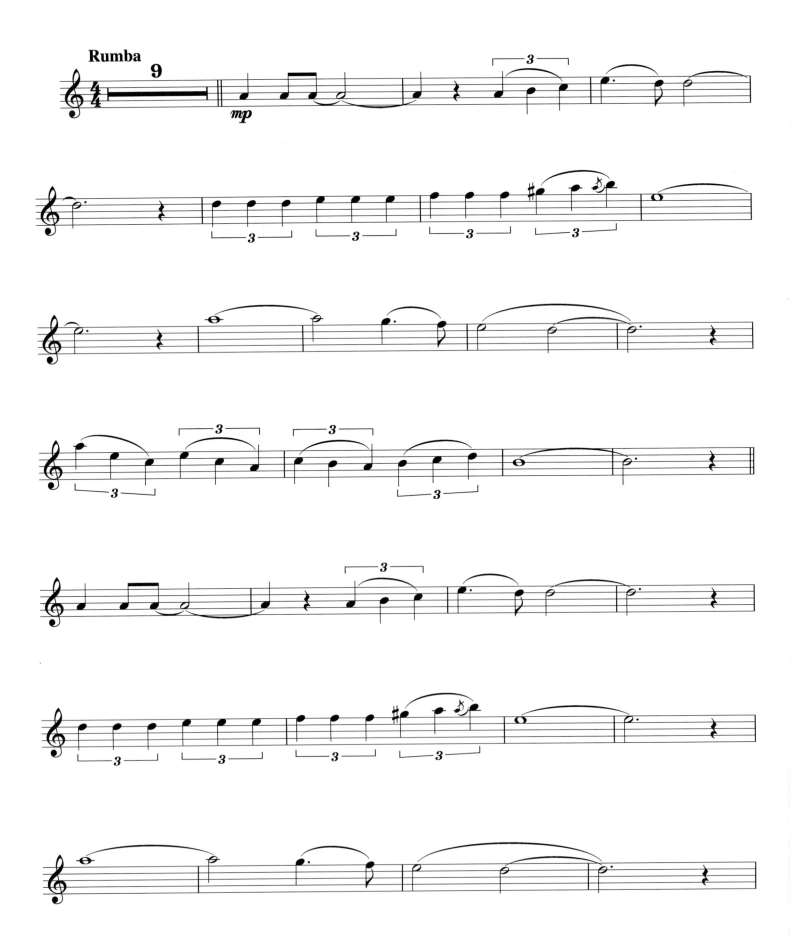

The Girl From Ipanema
(Garota De Ipanema)

Original Words by Vinicius De Moraes
Music by Antonio Carlos Jobim
English Words by Norman Gimbel

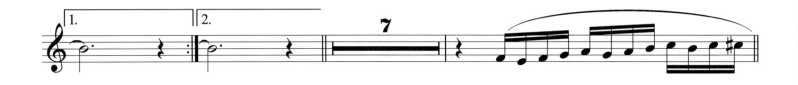

Guantanamera

Words Adapted by Julian Orbon from a poem by José Marti
Music Adaptation by Pete Seeger & Julian Orbon

p poco a poco cresc.

mp

3

3

mf

dim.

rit.

La Bamba

Traditional
Adapted & Arranged by Ritchie Valens

Lambada

Words & Music by Ulises Hermosa, Gonzales Hermosa, Alberto Maravi, Marcia Ferreira & Jose Ari
Music by Ulises Hermosa & Gonzales Hermosa

Mas Que Nada

Words & Music by Jorge Ben

Perhaps, Perhaps, Perhaps
(Quizas, Quizas, Quizas)

Original Words & Music by Osvaldo Farres
English Words by Joe Davis

Sway (Quien Sera)

Original Words & Music by Pablo Beltran Ruiz
English Words by Normal Gimbel

Oye Como Va

Words & Music by Tito Puente